Nighttime on the Beach

Written by Paige Cunningham
Illustrated by Janet Payne

Nighttime On the Beach
© 2013 by Paige Cunningham
Art Work © 2013 by Janet Payne
ISBN: 978-0-9895609-0-0
Library of Congress Control Number: 2013942857

Publication Design by
Ron Rollet
Published by
SeaGrove Press

To my family who showed me the wonders
of nature every day, in every season.

I would like to thank "KLINGSPOR's
Woodworking Shop" in North Carolina for
providing us with great service and quality
sandpaper for the illustrations.

Printed in the United States of America

SeaGrove Press
638 Sunset Blvd
Cape May, New Jersey 08204
seagrovepress@gmail.com

It's dark,
it's night,
the stars
are bright.

The sand is cool,
the waves they roar,
here we are,
down at the shore.

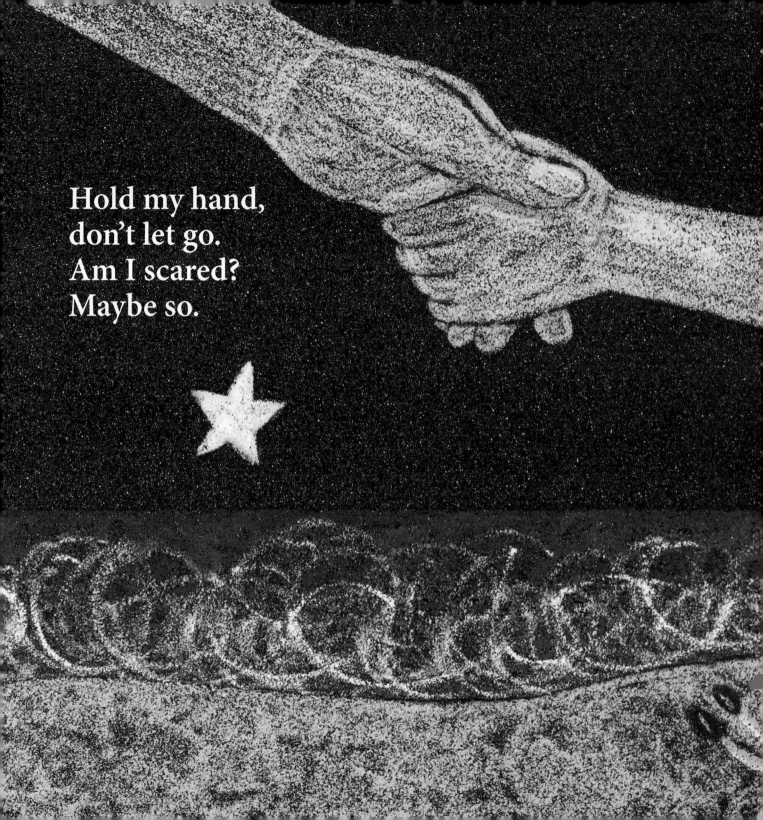

Hold my hand,
don't let go.
Am I scared?
Maybe so.

We search, we scan,
we glance around,
and then we spy,
a sandy mound.

We bend down low.
We shine our light.
We cheer and cheer,
what a great sight!!

In the sand.
In the hole.
Will it pop?
Will it roll?

We wait, we watch,
We wonder so.
Is it fast?
Or is it slow?

We look here.
We look there.
We must look,
everywhere.

Now we see it.
We shout hooray!
Quick we scream,
it's getting away!

We dart, we dash.
We squeal with delight.
It's so hard to see
in the dark of night!

Forward, backward,
side to side.
Then it stopped,
and tried to hide.

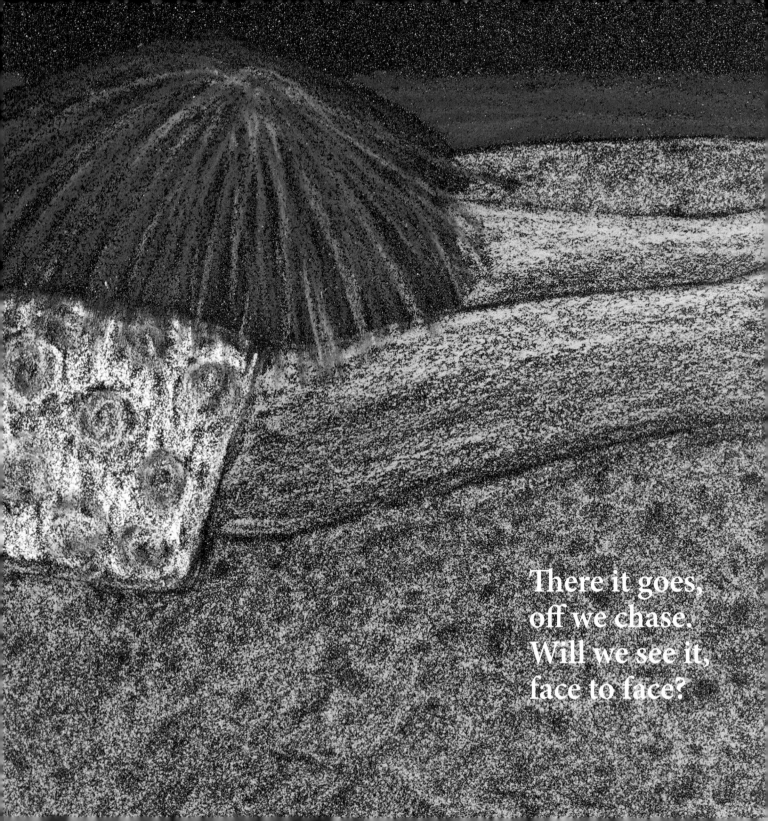

There it goes,
off we chase.
Will we see it,
face to face?

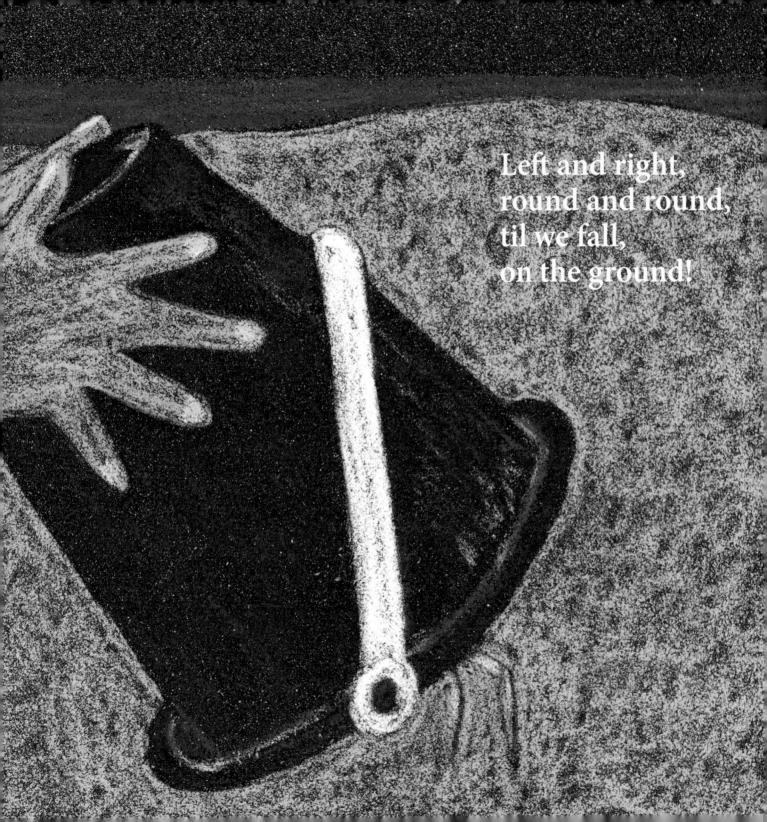

Left and right,
round and round,
til we fall,
on the ground!

Up we stand,
eyes are wide.
Dare we peek,
and look inside?

Could it be?
Is it true?
Yes, we whisper...

We caught YOU!

We look, we smile,
we wave hello.
Is it friend?
Or is it foe?

We smile and laugh.
We even giggle.
As we watch,
We see it wiggle.

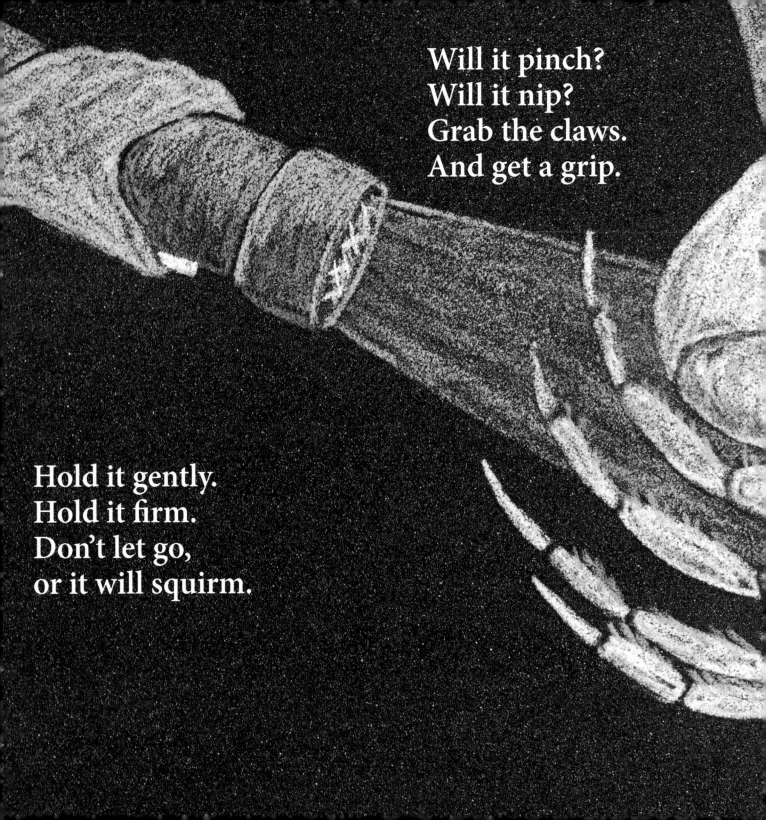

Will it pinch?
Will it nip?
Grab the claws.
And get a grip.

Hold it gently.
Hold it firm.
Don't let go,
or it will squirm.

It's tan.
It's speckled.
It's so pretty,
all bedeckled.

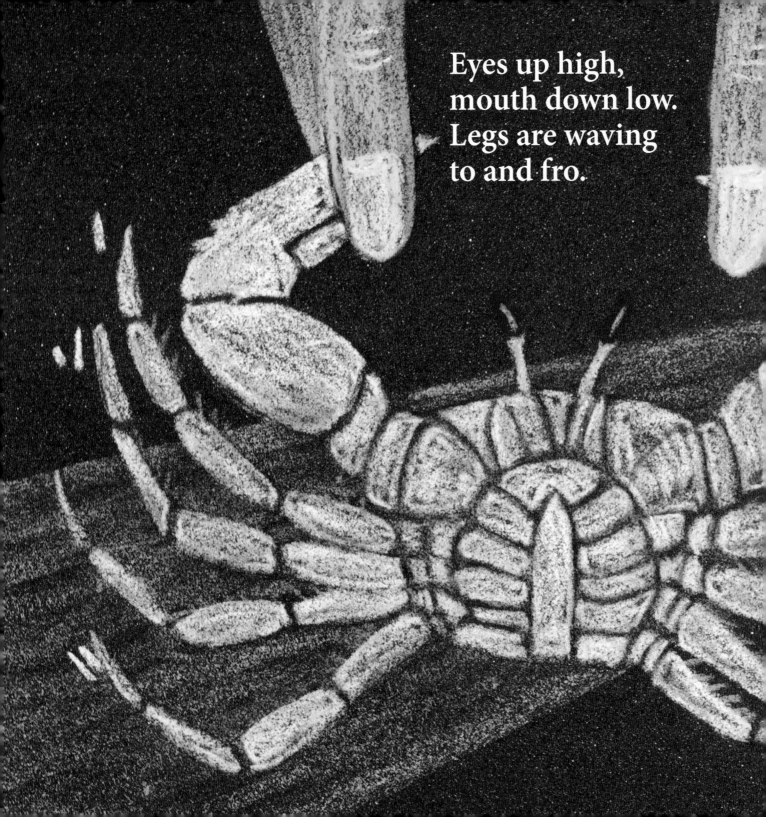

Eyes up high,
mouth down low.
Legs are waving
to and fro.

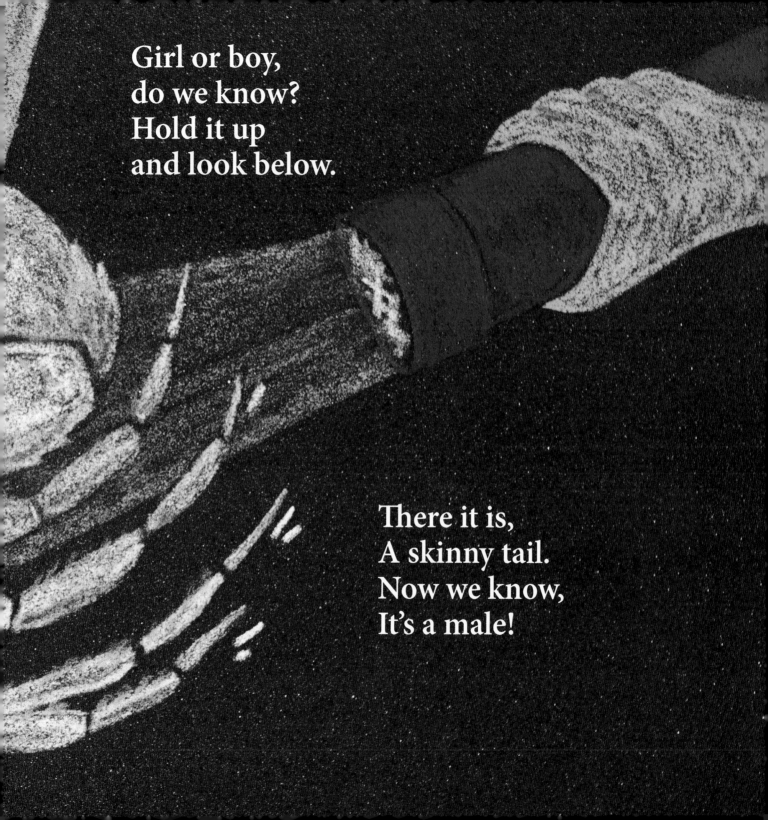

Girl or boy,
do we know?
Hold it up
and look below.

There it is,
A skinny tail.
Now we know,
It's a male!

Off you crawl
so you can eat.
Will you find,
a tasty treat?

Catch a clam.
Catch a flea.
Or you can feast,
on green algae.

This is fun,
we're sad to leave.
We're so happy
this summer eve!

You're awake,
your time to roam.
We must sleep,
so let's go home.

We look, we smile, we wave goodbye. We hope to see you next July.

It's dark,
It's night,
the stars
are bright.

More About Ghost Crabs

*The Latin name for ghost crab is Ocypode Quadrata, which means swift-footed square. A common name is "ghost crab" or "sand crab". Why do you think they have these names?

*Ghost crabs are a nocturnal creature. This means they are awake at night. Are you nocturnal?

*Ghost crabs can run up to10 mph forwards, backwards and even sideways! How fast can you run? Can you run sideways or backwards?

*Ghost crabs dig a tunnel in the sand up to 4 feet deep. How do you think they dig their tunnel? Can you find something that is 4 feet long? Why do they need a tunnel?

*Ghost crabs are considered a predator and scavenger because they eat a variety of things; baby birds and turtles, clams, sand fleas and even algae. What do you like to eat? What animals do you think would eat ghost crabs?

*Their eyes are on tall stalks so they can see 360 degrees. Why would they need to have such good vision?

*They can communicate by making sounds; rubbing their legs together, blowing bubbles, and rapping their claws on the sand. Why do you think they do this?

*They use their claws for many different reasons; to catch and eat food, to attract a mate and to defend themselves. How else might they protect themselves from predators?

*They can live up to 8 years old. How old are you?

✶Female ghost crabs carry 1000's of eggs under their wide triangle shaped tail. They will lay them in the water.

✶The young ghost crabs called larva live for 6 – 8 weeks floating in the sea as plankton and will wash ashore as apple seed size ghost crabs to live on the beach.

*Ghost crabs live on the sandy beaches on the East Coast of the United States. Can you find all the states where they might live, on a map? Some states where they inhabit have colder winters than others. Where do you think they go to hibernate?

Ghost Crab Viewing

*To view ghost crabs, visit a beach at dusk with a flashlight, when the weather is warm. Search for their sandy mounds and holes. Look at the waters edge, or anywhere, on the beach to spot them. If you think you see moving sand – it's probably a ghost crab!!! They are very good at playing ghost crab hide and seek!!

*Whenever you're out exploring nature, please remember to be respectful of the animals and their habitat.

*Only catch a ghost crab, if it won't harm the crab (or you), and after a few moments gently release it back on the sand.

*What other creatures can you find on the beach at night?

Paige Cunningham, naturalist and art educator, grew up in Easton, CT and currently lives in West Cape May, NJ with her husband and 3 cats. Paige has been leading ghost crab walks on the beaches of Cape May since 2003. "It's so fun to show people what nature is doing after dark! To hear their laughs, see their smiles and wide eyes when they spot their first ghost crab scurrying on the beach, makes my night"

Janet Payne, illustrator and teaching artist, works in a variety of mediums including, printmaking and pastels. Janet lives in Cape May, New Jersey with her cat Mo. She enjoys sailing and traveling to warm sandy beaches and looking for treasures and ghost crabs. This is her second book collaboration with Paige Cunningham.

Made in the USA
Charleston, SC
21 July 2014